GRADE

3

The 2005–2007 Syllabus should be
requirements, especially those for s
sight-reading. Attention should be
Notices on the inside front cover, whe
any changes.

The syllabus is obtainable from music retailers or from
the Services Department, The Associated Board of the Royal
Schools of Music, 24 Portland Place, London W1B 1LU,
United Kingdom (please send a stamped addressed C5
(162mm × 229mm) envelope).

In exam centres outside the UK, information and syllabuses
may be obtained from the Local Representative.

CONTENTS

Where appropriate, pieces in this volume have been checked with original source material
and edited as necessary for instructional purposes. Fingering, phrasing, bowing,
metronome marks and the editorial realization of ornaments (where given) are for
guidance only; they are not comprehensive or obligatory.

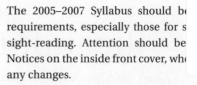

**DO NOT
PHOTOCOPY
© MUSIC**

Alternative pieces for this grade

© 2004 by The Associated Board of the Royal Schools of Music

No part of this publication may be copied or reproduced in
any form or by any means without the prior permission of
the publisher.

Music origination by Andrew Jones.
Cover by Økvik Design.
Printed in England by Caligraving Ltd,
Thetford, Norfolk.

Rigaudon and Trio

from *Water Music*, Suite No. 3 in G, HWV 350

Transcribed and edited by
Richard Jones

HANDEL

This rigaudon and trio are drawn from the third of the three orchestral suites that make up Handel's *Water Music*. This collection of pieces takes its name from the circumstances of its first performance: a royal water party on the River Thames on 17 July 1717, accompanied by Handel's music, 'which His Majesty liked so well that he caused it to be played over three times in going and returning.' The rigaudon is a lively French dance in duple time, similar to the bourrée. This rigaudon was originally scored for oboes, strings and continuo. The slurs are authentic, but all dynamics are editorial suggestions only. Crotchets might be lightly detached (without lifting the bow off the string). In the exam the da capo should be played, but none of the internal repeats.

Sources: *The Celebrated Water Musick in seven parts* (London: J. Walsh, c.1733);
Handel's Celebrated Water Musick compleat: set for the harpsicord (London: J. Walsh, 1743)

TRIO

Fine

cresc.

Rigaudon D.C.

 A:2

Watkins' Ale

Arranged by
Edward Huws Jones

ANON. ENGLISH

This delightful and rather cheeky Elizabethan melody and its variations are adapted from versions in the 'Fitzwilliam Virginal Book' and the 'Welde Lute Book'. Your performance can be as lively as you like; the rhythm in bb. 13–16 needs to be crisp. EHJ

© Copyright 2000 by Boosey & Hawkes Music Publishers Ltd
Reproduced from *The Early Music Fiddler* by permission. All enquiries for this piece apart from the exams should be addressed to Boosey & Hawkes Music Publishers Ltd, Aldwych House, 71-91 Aldwych, London WC2B 4HN.

Moderato

First movement from Sonatina, Anh. 5/1

Arranged by
Eta Cohen and Richard Drakeford

BEETHOVEN

The young Beethoven received piano and violin lessons from his father, and made his first public appearance at a concert in 1778, at the age of seven. This Moderato is taken from a pair of sonatinas for piano, listed as Anhang (appendix) 5 in G. Kinsky and H. Halm: *Das Werk Beethovens*.

Romance

No. 3 from *Eight Easy Pieces*

BAKLANOVA

From Edition Peters No. 5703 Baklanova: *Eight Easy Pieces*

© Copyright C.F. Peters Frankfurt

Reproduced by permission of C.F. Peters Music Publishers Frankfurt/M., Leipzig, London, New York. All enquiries for this piece apart from the exams should be addressed to Peters Edition Ltd, 10–12 Baches Street, London N1 6DN.

Waltz
Op. 39 No. 15

B:2

Arranged by
Shin'ichi Suzuki

BRAHMS

Brahms's Op. 39 Waltzes were originally written for piano duet, then adapted by him for piano solo. They celebrate a dance form associated with Vienna, his adopted city.

Sole publishers for the world except Japan: Summy-Birchard Inc., distributed exclusively by Warner Bros. Publications Inc. Reproduced by permission of Faber Music Ltd. All rights reserved. All enquiries for this piece apart from the exams should be addressed to Faber Music Ltd, 3 Queen Square, London WC1N 3AU.

Air de ballet

No. 4 from *Petite école de la mélodie*, Op. 123, Book 1

C. DANCLA

The violinist Charles Dancla (1817–1907) was a member of a very musical family. His two brothers and sister were accomplished musicians, and the four players formed a chamber group that performed regularly in Paris in the 1840s. Some of the dynamics in this edition have been added for guidance.

Down by the Riverside

Arranged by
Edward Huws Jones

ANON. SPIRITUAL

This well-known spiritual begins: 'Gonna lay down my sword and shield, down by the riverside... Ain't gonna study war no more.' This bluesy arrangement of the tune needs a relaxed bowing style and swung quavers. EHJ

Shepherdess

from *Folk Melodies*

Arranged by
Helena Dunicz-Niwińska and Maria Dziewulska

LUTOSŁAWSKI

This piece by Polish composer Witold Lutosławski (1913–94) is based on a folk-tune from the Podlasie region in the east of the country, known for its forests and wetlands. The bowing symbols indicate the following:

⊓ with the lower part of the bow
⊔ with the whole bow

Ain't Misbehavin'

Arranged by
Edward Huws Jones

WALLER and BROOKS

Ain't Misbehavin' is a classic jazz tune from the 1920s. The style calls for a natural, relaxed use of the bow, sometimes slurring across the beat. As is often the case in jazz, the quavers should be swung. EHJ

© 1929 EMI Mills Music Inc., USA
Redwood Music Ltd, London NW1 8BD (music). Reproduced by permission of Faber Music Ltd. All Rights Reserved. All enquiries for this piece apart from the exams should be addressed to Faber Music Ltd, 3 Queen Square, London WC1N 3AU.

Checklist of Scales and Arpeggios

Candidates and teachers may find this checklist useful in learning the requirements of the grade. Full details of the forms of the various requirements, including details of rhythms, starting notes and bowing patterns, are given in the syllabus and in the scale books published by the Board.

Grade 3

			separate bows						slurred					
									two quavers to a bow					
Major Scales	E Major	1 Octave												
	G Major	2 Octaves												
	A Major	2 Octaves												
	B♭ Major	2 Octaves												
	D Major	2 Octaves												
									two quavers to a bow					
Minor Scales *(melodic or harmonic)*	E Minor	1 Octave												
	G Minor	2 Octaves												
	A Minor	2 Octaves												
	D Minor	2 Octaves												
									not applicable					
Chromatic Scales	on G	1 Octave												
	on D	1 Octave												
	on A	1 Octave												
									three notes to a bow					
Major Arpeggios	E Major	1 Octave												
	G Major	2 Octaves												
	A Major	2 Octaves												
	B♭ Major	2 Octaves												
	D Major	2 Octaves												
									three notes to a bow					
Minor Arpeggios	E Minor	1 Octave												
	G Minor	2 Octaves												
	A Minor	2 Octaves												
	D Minor	2 Octaves												
									not applicable					
Dominant Sevenths	in C	1 Octave												
	in G	1 Octave												
	in D	1 Octave												

GRADE 3

The 2005–2007 Syllabus should be read for details of requirements, especially those for scales, aural tests and sight-reading. Attention should be paid to the Special Notices on the inside front cover, where warning is given of any changes.

The syllabus is obtainable from music retailers or from the Services Department, The Associated Board of the Royal Schools of Music, 24 Portland Place, London W1B 1LU, United Kingdom (please send a stamped addressed C5 (162mm × 229mm) envelope).

In exam centres outside the UK, information and syllabuses may be obtained from the Local Representative.

REQUIREMENTS

SCALES AND ARPEGGIOS (from memory)
in E major; E minor (one octave)
G, A, Bb, D majors; G, A, D minors (two octaves)

Scales
in the above keys (minors in melodic *or* harmonic form at candidate's choice):
(i)   separate bows
(ii) slurred, two quavers to a bow

Chromatic Scales
starting on open strings G, D and A (one octave):
separate bows, even notes

Arpeggios
the common chords of the above keys:
(i)   separate bows, even notes
(ii) slurred, three notes to a bow

Dominant Sevenths
in the keys of C, G and D (starting on open strings G, D and A and resolving on the tonic) (one octave):
separate bows, even notes

PLAYING AT SIGHT (see current syllabus)

AURAL TESTS (see current syllabus)

THREE PIECES   *page*

**DO NOT
PHOTOCOPY
© MUSIC**

Candidates must prepare three pieces, one from each of the three Lists, A, B and C. Candidates may choose from the pieces printed in this volume or any other piece listed for the grade. A full list is given in the current syllabus.

Where appropriate, pieces in this volume have been checked with original source material and edited as necessary for instructional purposes. Fingering, phrasing, bowing, metronome marks and the editorial realization of ornaments (where given) are for guidance only; they are not comprehensive or obligatory.

Rigaudon and Trio

from *Water Music*, Suite No. 3 in G, HWV 350

Transcribed and edited by
Richard Jones

HANDEL

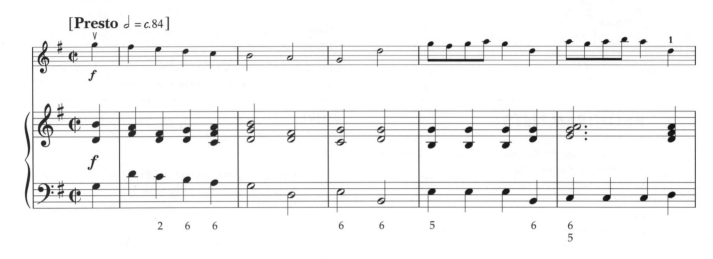

This rigaudon and trio are drawn from the third of the three orchestral suites that make up Handel's *Water Music*. This collection of pieces takes its name from the circumstances of its first performance: a royal water party on the River Thames on 17 July 1717, accompanied by Handel's music, 'which His Majesty liked so well that he caused it to be played over three times in going and returning.' The rigaudon is a lively French dance in duple time, similar to the bourrée. This rigaudon was originally scored for oboes, strings and continuo. The slurs are authentic, but all dynamics are editorial suggestions only. Crotchets might be lightly detached (without lifting the bow off the string). In the exam the da capo should be played, but none of the internal repeats.

Sources: *The Celebrated Water Musick in seven parts* (London: J. Walsh, *c.*1733);
Handel's Celebrated Water Musick compleat: set for the harpsicord (London: J. Walsh, 1743)

TRIO

Rigaudon D.C.

Watkins' Ale

Arranged by
Edward Huws Jones

ANON. ENGLISH

This delightful and rather cheeky Elizabethan melody and its variations are adapted from versions in the 'Fitzwilliam Virginal Book' and the 'Welde Lute Book'. Your performance can be as lively as you like; the rhythm in bb. 13–16 needs to be crisp. EHJ

Reproduced from *The Early Music Fiddler* by permission. All enquiries for this piece apart from the exams should be addressed to Boosey & Hawkes Music Publishers Ltd, Aldwych House, 71-91 Aldwych, London WC2B 4HN.

Moderato

First movement from Sonatina, Anh. 5/1

Arranged by
Eta Cohen and Richard Drakeford

BEETHOVEN

At a moderate speed [♩ = c. 100]

The young Beethoven received piano and violin lessons from his father, and made his first public appearance at a concert in 1778, at the age of seven. This Moderato is taken from a pair of sonatinas for piano, listed as Anhang (appendix) 5 in G. Kinsky and H. Halm: *Das Werk Beethovens*.

Romance

No. 3 from *Eight Easy Pieces*

BAKLANOVA

From Edition Peters No. 5703 Baklanova: *Eight Easy Pieces*

© Copyright C.F. Peters Frankfurt

B:2

Waltz
Op. 39 No. 15

Arranged by
Shin'ichi Suzuki

BRAHMS

Brahms's Op. 39 Waltzes were originally written for piano duet, then adapted by him for piano solo. They celebrate a dance form associated with Vienna, his adopted city.

© 1978 Dr Shin'ichi Suzuki

B:3

Air de ballet

No. 4 from *Petite école de la mélodie*, Op. 123, Book 1

C. DANCLA

The violinist Charles Dancla (1817–1907) was a member of a very musical family. His two brothers and sister were accomplished musicians, and the four players formed a chamber group that performed regularly in Paris in the 1840s. Some of the dynamics in this edition have been added for guidance.

© 2004 by The Associated Board of the Royal Schools of Music

C:1

Down by the Riverside

Arranged by
Edward Huws Jones

ANON. SPIRITUAL

This well-known spiritual begins: 'Gonna lay down my sword and shield, down by the riverside... Ain't gonna study war no more.' This bluesy arrangement of the tune needs a relaxed bowing style and swung quavers. EHJ

Shepherdess

from *Folk Melodies*

Arranged by
Helena Dunicz-Niwińska and Maria Dziewulska

LUTOSŁAWSKI

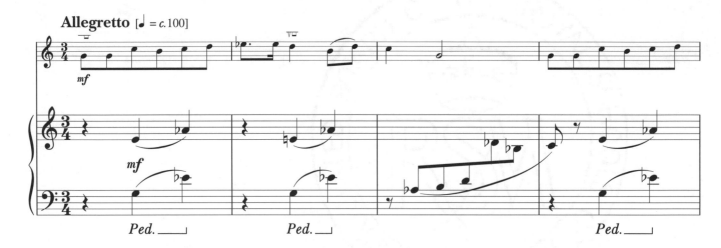

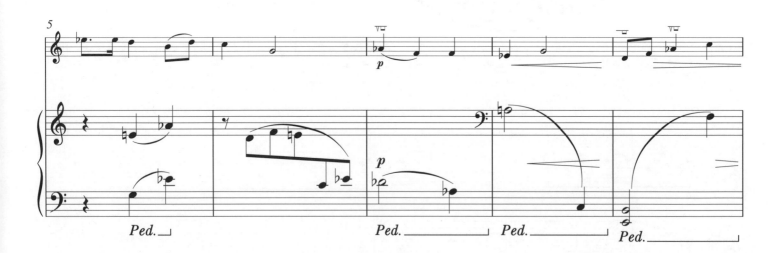

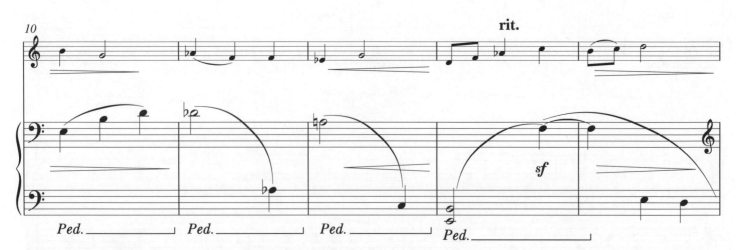

This piece by Polish composer Witold Lutosławski (1913–94) is based on a folk-tune from the Podlasie region in the east of the country, known for its forests and wetlands. The bowing symbols indicate the following:

⊓ with the lower part of the bow
⊔ with the whole bow

Ain't Misbehavin'

Arranged by
Edward Huws Jones

WALLER and BROOKS

Ain't Misbehavin' is a classic jazz tune from the 1920s. The style calls for a natural, relaxed use of the bow, sometimes slurring across the beat. As is often the case in jazz, the quavers should be swung. EHJ